JUMBO
COLORING AND ACTIVITY BOOK

MISS BABY

Center Stage and her Lil Sister are always en pointe!

Every day is the start of a new chapter for the Storybook Club. What adventures await them?

S OT T ε DIϜϜε εNCε

Which picture of Pink Baby is different from the others?

A

B

C

D

Your Answer:

Answer: C

It Baby is a total trendsetter.
She always knows the next big look.

Golden sands, crystal blue water,
and perfect wavy hair —the beach is our bae!

TIC-TAC-TOE

Challenge your BFF!

The Glam Club

cuties are all class.

Did somebody say #selfie?

D.J. is spinnin' some sick beats.
It's time to pump up the party!

The Cosplay Club loves everything kawaii!

Genie isn't waiting for a magic lamp, she's making her stage dreams come true right now!

For the darlings of the Opposites Club,
differences are the spice of life.

GET GLAM

It Baby has chosen YOU to design a fabulous new outfit just for her. Draw it below, and then decorate the outfit with your classiest colors.

Kitty Queen and her Lil Sister are feline fashion icons.
Their style is pure purr-fection!

Let's bounce! Hoops MVP is teaching her
Lil Sister how to tear up the court.

COPY CAT

Use the grid below to create a purr-fect paw-trait of Troublemaker.

Is it a bird? Is it a plane?
No, it's Super B.B. and she's ready to save the day!

Baby, it's cold outside. Time to snuggle up
with the cool cuties in the Chill Out Club.

Lil Dollface is ga-ga for glamour,
just like her faux-fur-loving big sister.

Royal High-ney has high standards—she won't accept anything less than the very best.

© MGA

READY FOR MY SELFIE

Leading Baby's selfie game is always on point!
Color her in and then add a cute hashtag.

We've got spirit, yes we do,
we've got spirit, how 'bout you?

The Retro Club girls are the original style queens.
Classics never go out of fashion.

Sugar Queen is nuts about the stage!
She belongs in the spotlight.

All those baby MCs ain't got nothin'
on Honey Bun and her Lil Sister.

MATCHING

Draw a line to match each Chill Out Club gal to their name!

Brrr B.B.

Cozy Babe

Snow Angel

Miss Baby has glamour and grace for days!
This pageant girl is destined for the runway.

Rocker lives and breathes music.
She'll take a microphone and guitar
over a pacifier and bottle any day.

WORD SEARCH

Help Teacher's Pet find the names of the
L.O.L. Surprise! clubs in the grid below.

S	T	O	R	Y	B	O	O	K
F	H	G	A	A	B	B	M	K
T	I	O	G	L	A	M	P	S
K	P	M	W	P	Q	F	L	P
L	H	R	Z	S	M	N	J	I
M	O	Y	Z	O	R	T	E	R
Q	P	D	C	C	G	H	J	I
V	T	H	E	A	T	E	R	T
P	C	I	T	E	L	H	T	A

STORYBOOK　　**SPIRIT**

GLAM　　**RETRO**

HIP HOP　　**COSPLAY**

THEATER　　**ATHLETIC**

Why say it when you can sing it?
The Glee Club girls have music in their soul.

The Athletic Club tots have the skills to dominate any sports scene. On the track, court, field, wherever—they've got game!

The Chill Out Club are such cool cuties.

Brrr-illiant!

Fancy and Fresh may be very different,
but that doesn't stop them being BFFs.
Opposites attract, after all!

MATCHING

Which two pictures of Cherry are the same?

A

B

C

Your
Answer:

D

Lil Majorette is a marching band star in the making!
There's no better example to follow than her
big sister—no one rallies a crowd like her!

© MGA

Starry-eyed Luxe loves all things lavish and lush.

Grab your shiniest outfit and join the #sparklesquad!

Let your imagination run wild, like Curious Q.T.
Where will it take you today?

SPOT T E DIFFERENCE

Which picture of Jitterbug is different from the others?

A

B

C

Your
Answer:

D

© MGA

Lights, camera, action!
Theater Club is ready to hit the stage.

It's impossible to keep a straight face around Pranksta. She'll make you laugh 'til you cry—oopsie!

Baby Cat is paw-sitively smitten with the stage.

M.C. Swag and her Lil Sister love spittin' rhymes
b4 naptime. Time for a rap battle!

It's not easy being Queen Bee.
But if the crown fits, she'll wear it!

LARGE AND SMALL

Color all of the large pictures of Lil Fancy!

Breakin' hearts never looked so cute!
Heartbreaker loves fierce fashion fit for a queen.

Breakin' hearts never looked so cute!

Miss Punk proves you can rock a pair of killer boots
and funky hair, and still be a princess.

Double the trouble!

Peek-a-boo

Cosmic Queen is an out-of-this-world BFF. She believes you can achieve anything if you reach for the stars!

Pink Baby is a vintage style icon.
She was reppin' retro before retro was a thing!

Purple Queen and her Lil Sister are total party animals! Every day is a celebration with these sparkle-rific sisters.

PARTY LIKE IT'S 9:59 PM!

U DON'T GOTTA BE COOL 2 RULE MY WORLD

CHILL OUT

Use the grid below to create a fabulous portait of Brrr B.B.

The
Retro Club
gals believe classic is always cool.

Stardust Queen gets her sparkle straight
from the cosmos. She's a rising star,
ready to blow your mind.

Glitter Queen and her Lil Sis glitterally can't get enough of the sparkly stuff.

The Athletic Club cuties **run the world!**

SQUARES

Taking turns, connect a line from one star to another. If you write the line that completes a box, write your initial in that box. The person with the most squares at the end of the game is the winner!

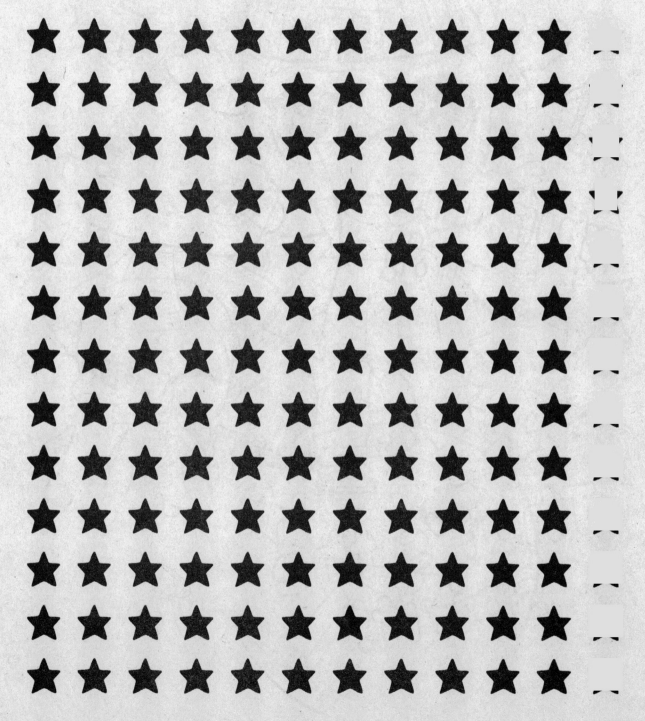

© MGA

Teamwork makes the dream work.

Posh is the queen of the snug-and-stylish look.
Any outfit can be completed with a cute beret!

Hops is forever getting lost in her daydreams
and running late for very important dates.

Brrr B.B.

is one chilled out cutie.

WORD SEARCH

Find the names in the grid below.

S	N	O	W	A	N	G	E	L
W	H	G	A	O	B	B	M	S
X	A	O	L	U	X	E	P	K
D	F	M	W	S	Q	F	L	R
M	A	J	O	R	E	T	T	E
H	N	Y	Z	W	R	T	E	K
S	C	D	C	C	G	H	J	C
O	Y	B	B	B	O	P	R	O
P	B	O	N	B	O	N	T	R

SNOW ANGEL   LUXE

BON BON   ROCKER

FANCY   POSH

MAJORETTE   B.B. BOP

Every day is a costume party for the Cosplay Club.
You can be anyone you want to be!

Lil Merbaby and her big sis live the
mermaid life both on and off the stage.

MATCHING

Draw a line to match each gal to their shadow!

Teacher's Pet and her Lil Sister are the brightest of the bunch. They love to study and learn.

Splash Queen is making waves in the Glitterati.
She brings the shimmer and sparkle
to seaside glamour.

DESIGNER DOLL

The L.O.L. Surprise! dolls can never have too many BFFs!
Use your imagination to create a brand-new doll.

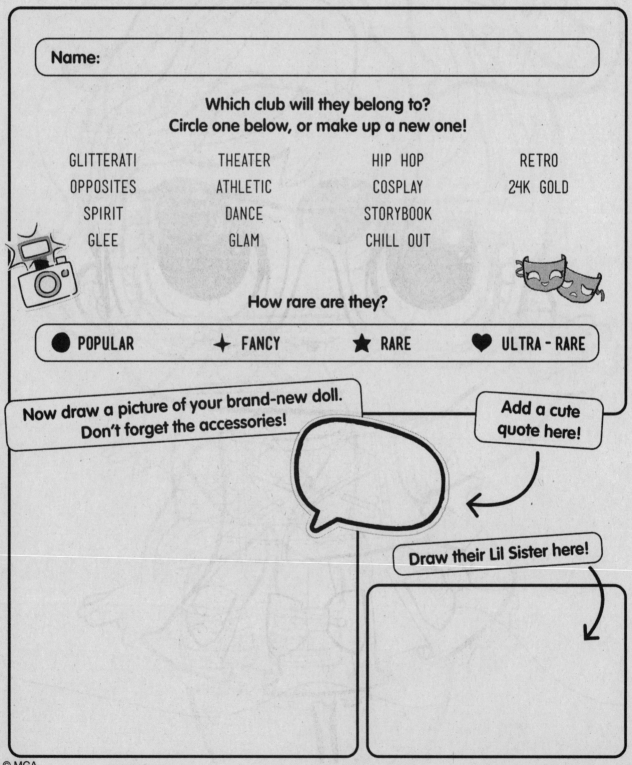

Name:

Which club will they belong to?
Circle one below, or make up a new one!

GLITTERATI	THEATER	HIP HOP	RETRO
OPPOSITES	ATHLETIC	COSPLAY	24K GOLD
SPIRIT	DANCE	STORYBOOK	
GLEE	GLAM	CHILL OUT	

How rare are they?

● POPULAR　　✦ FANCY　　★ RARE　　♥ ULTRA – RARE

Now draw a picture of your brand-new doll.
Don't forget the accessories!

Add a cute
quote here!

Draw their Lil Sister here!

Dressed head to toe in perfect pastels,
Bon Bon is as cute as a button.

Roller Sk8er ain't got time for h8ers.
She's too busy practicing the
sweetest tricks around.

A-MAZE-ING

Lead Super B.B. through the maze to find Su-Purr Kitty.

Diva knows the best person you can be is yourself.
Individuality never goes out of style!

Punk 4 lyf

MISS PUNK

Born to be bad.

Court Champ has got game.

MISSING PIECE

Can you find the missing piece of the puzzle?

A

B

C

Crystal Queen lives for all things sparkly.
Diamond tiaras, diamond rings—
she wants all bling, everything!

© MGA

B.B. Bop is teaching her Lil Sister to be strong and independent. It's your time to shine!

When Coconut Q.T.'s not on the stage,
you can find her partying at a luau.
Grab a lei and join the hula dancing!

Howdy, partner! Line Dancer and her
Lil Sister are waiting for you to join them—
so pull on your dancing shoes and cut loose!

Ice Sk8er and her Lil Sister are the coolest duo on the ice. They sk8 rings around the competition.